DEAR SON

from you to me©

A JOURNAL OF A LIFETIME

Dear

This journal is a gift with a twist . . . it's from you to me.

When we are children we are always asking questions . . . well now I have some more for you. Please could you answer them in the way that only you know how and then give the book back to me.

There might be a couple of questions that you would prefer not to answer, so don't worry, just answer the others as well as you can . . . I won't mind.

People say that we all have at least one book in us and this will be one of yours. The story of you and me that I will treasure forever.

Thank you,

with love

What are some of your earliest memories?

What do you think people thought of you as a child?

What are some of the things you like doing in your life?

Tell me about some of the best things that have happened to you . . .

What have been some of your favourite holidays?

How would you describe yourself?

Who or what has been the biggest influence on you?

Who did you most admire or look up to when you were younger and why?

What was the first piece of music you bought
and in what format?

What piece/s of music would you choose to be in your 'top 10' favourite tracks?

What is the naughtiest thing you have ever done?

Tell me something about yourself that you think no one else will know . . .

What are some of your favourite ways of spending a weekend?

Describe some of your fondest memories of the
times we have spent together . . .

What are a few of your favourite things?

If you were an animal . . . what type of animal would you be, and why?

What do you think are your greatest strengths
and weaknesses?

What have you found most difficult in your life?

With the benefit of hindsight, what would you do differently?

Describe some of the things you remember about your school / college days . . .

Tell me about some of your most enjoyable
experiences at school / college . . .

What have you been best at during your time at school / college?

Describe the favourite teachers you have had . . .
what is it about them you like and/or respect?

What do you think I am most proud of about you?

Tell me about your best friends . . . what do you like about them?

What do you enjoy doing with your friends?

How would you compare your male and female friends and how you get on with them?

What do you think your friends like most and least about you?

What do you like most about family life?

How well do you get on with the different people in our family?

What do you think I like most about you?

What do you think I worry about most with you?

What have you most enjoyed doing with our family . . . and least enjoyed?

What do I do that you appreciate and would like me to carry on doing?

What do I do that you do not appreciate and would like me to stop doing?

What do you like most, and least, about other
members of our family?

Tell me about the family values you have learnt
along the way that you would like to pass on . . .

What would you draw on from your childhood and upbringing when raising your own children?

This page is for you to write about other members of our family . . .

What advice would you like to give me or other members of our family?

What ideas have you had about what you
wanted to do when you grew up and are things
going to plan?

What sort of person did you think you would grow to be and have you got there yet?

Where would you like to travel to?

Where might you like to live and why?

Tell me about some of the things you would still like to do in your life . . .

What would you still love us to do together?

Are there any new things you would like to do with your friends?

If you won the Lottery . . . what would you do
with the money?

If you could travel in time . . . when and where would you go?

If you were granted three wishes . . . what would they be and why?

Who do you most admire and why?

What is the best piece of advice you have been
given . . . and how has it influenced you?

What qualities would you most like to be known for?

Tell me about the dreams you have for your life . . .

Tell me your goals & aspirations for the next
5 / 10 / 20 years . . .

What can I do to help you achieve what you
want?

And now your chance to tell me some other personal stories that you want to share . . .

AND FINALLY FOR THE RECORD ...

What is your full name?

What is your date of birth?

What colour are your eyes?

How tall are you?

What blood group are you?

What date did you complete this story for me?

THANK YOU

for taking the time to complete this journal.
I will treasure it forever.

DEAR SON

from you to me©

The Timeless Collection, first published by **JOURNALS OF A LIFETIME**,
an imprint of **FROM YOU TO ME LTD** in September 2017

There are nine titles in the collection:
Dear Mum, Dad, Grandma, Grandad, Daughter, Son, Sister, Brother and Friend.

To personalise journals and books, as well as purchase
other products produced by us, please go to

WWW.FROMYOUTOME.COM

Printed and bound in China.
This paper is manufactured from pulp sourced from
forests that are legally and sustainably managed.

FROM YOU TO ME, Waterhouse, Waterhouse Lane, Monkton Combe, Bath, BA2 7JA, UK

3 5 7 9 11 13 15 14 12 10 8 6 4 2

Copyright © 2017 FROM YOU TO ME LTD

ISBN 978-1-907860-37-9

A JOURNAL OF A LIFETIME